CH00794069

ILYA is a professional comic bc
Since 1987 his work has appeare
Marvel, DC and Dark Horse in the L
numerous independent companies
the *Manga Drawing Kit* for Thunder Bay Press. Other bookwork includes: *Countdown* and *Time Warp*, two collections of his award-winning graphic novel series *The End of the Century Club*; *A Bowl of Rice*, for Amnesty International; *It's Dark in London*, a noir anthology from Serpent's Tail; and *Skidmarks*, a charming kitchen-sink drama series. ILYA also designs and tutors workshops on the art of comics and manga for colleges, galleries, libraries, schools and prisons, across the UK as well as abroad.

Recent clients include BBC Online, The Royal Academy of Arts, and the *Independent on Sunday* – all things his proud parents have heard of. Luckily there's always manga to keep them stumped. His ambition in life is to make more manga.

The Mammoth Book of **BEST NEW**
manga

2

Edited by ILYA

ROBINSON
London

Constable & Robinson Ltd
3 The Lanchesters
162 Fulham Palace Road
London W6 9ER
www.constablerobinson.com

First published in the UK by Robinson,
an imprint of Constable & Robinson Ltd 2007

A copy of the British Library Cataloguing in
Publication Data is available from the British Library.

ISBN 978-1-84529-642-1

Printed and bound in the EU

1 3 5 7 9 10 8 6 4 2

Contents

Introduction

Worlds Apart... Drawn Together

The Mammoth Book of Best New Manga Volume Two (or *BNM 2* to its friends) is designed to be a rolling showcase of international talent. This is to reflect the ever-growing trend for the creation of original comic strip stories – crucially, those inspired and influenced by Japanese manga and anime – among artists all around the globe.

Thanks to the worldwide web, we bring you offerings from as far afield as Singapore and Scotland, from Auckland, New Zealand to Cleveland, USA. In recognition of China's lightning growth as a superpower, there are a number of offerings by creators (even if they happen to be brought up in Sweden, or are living in Edinburgh), including Nana Li, Yishan Li, and our cover artist, Ivy Ling. Copies of *Best New Manga's* Volume One also made their way to Malaysia, resulting in a flurry of submissions from what is obviously a very lively (and hugely accomplished) manga scene there. This volume showcases some of Malaysia's finest mangaka: Ivan Song, Eve Yap and Cubbie.

With a little help from our friends, in Volume Three, scheduled for 2008, we plan to take a closer look at what's going on with manga in Italy and Greece. Australia and New Zealand are quite close to the islands of Japan, where manga originated, and we also hope to discover some local talent there. As yet we've barely scratched the USA – welcome, then, to Niki Smith and Anna Mercedes (who did).

Check Out our Brand New Colour Section

Following the success of the hugely influential, feature-length animated film *Akira* in the late 1980s, through to the likes of *Naruto* and *Dragonball Z* on our televisions today, for most people outside of Japan our first experience of manga comes in the forms of animated cartoon adaptations – anime, and not manga. That makes our home-grown variations of manga look different from the get-go. The drawing styles often have thicker outlines; bolder, simpler shapes; cel-animation style colouring; and, yes, our manga comes quite naturally in colour. With still so few comics being published in our native countries in comparison with Japan, the internet as yet remains a primary outlet for the great majority of this material. So when it comes to the creators of today's best new manga, they are for the most part making their manga in full colour – because they want to, and because they can.

In Japan manga mainly come in black and white, which is reflected in the small selection of material that is currently being translated and imported from there. Even in Japan though, full-colour manga are not unheard of: there is nothing inherently manga about being in black and white. The weekly and monthly *zasshi* – the magazine anthologies that *Best New Manga,* even as an annual, most closely resembles – usually contain at least some colour content. The lead strip in any given issue often kicks off with a sequence in colour, a feature preserved when those same strip serials are compiled into their own book collections (the *tankubon* and *bunkobon* paperback book formats resembling those we get in the West). Not only do these titles have print-runs in the millions, the manga studios have to produce many, many pages every week just to keep up with the demand. Only these bulk economics prevent the Japanese from using more colour in their manga – and if they could, they would.

So the new colour section you will find at the centre of this book is our best reflection of what is already happening, but only a glimpse of what is actually possible. Manga is by now a household word. Rather than cater to and be limited by any existing fan base, *Best New Manga* is very much explicitly aimed at a wider market – the general public excited by Studio Ghibli films and the cartoon serials on their TVs, and wanting a broad-based introduction to the form as it exists, and continues to develop, both inside and outside of Japan.

Critical Mass

Manga (and anime) within Japan is a mass-market medium. Such is the strength of the material being created, it has the very real potential to break out of any fandom or self-imposed ghetto and become the same anywhere else in the world. The modern mainstream audience expects colour – in its comics, as with its films and everything else. Left to their own devices, instinctively and quite spontaneously, the rising generations of mangaka (creators of manga) are making their manga in both black and white and in very significant and surprising numbers in full colour.

It certainly seems to make sense that if those two factors are put together – the demand for full colour entertainment, and the supply of full colour manga – the result will be an exponential growth of the manga reading market beyond anything yet seen. And this, surely, will be the very best reflection of manga as it is enjoyed in its homeland of Japan, as a mass-market medium catering to and enjoyed by almost everybody.

Let's work to make sure that happens. If you agree (or even if you don't!), be sure to talk it up and show this book to everyone you know, whether or not you think they might be interested. Quite frankly, the more copies the book sells the more chance there is of springing for even more pages in colour – and then manga sells even better, and so on. Many manga stories are created in black and white for aesthetic or other reasons, but it would be great (and more accurate!) for us to be able to showcase the many new strips that are daily being created just as their creators meant them to be seen – in full colour. Every contributor should at least be given that option, so that they may choose for themselves whether to show their work in black and white or colour. For every story like *The Forgotten Incident of San Sabian*, very deliberately best expressed in black and white, there are others, such as *November*, or *Strum*, where the strip would have been created in full colour if only that presentation were possible.

An Explosion Waiting To Happen

Even running to a mammoth 544 (count 'em) pages, we could still have easily filled this book twice over. We'll never be able to print enough examples of all of the fabulous mutations of manga currently cropping up all over the world, unless we start publishing twice a year – something we'd gladly do if we didn't also think it'd drive us (even more) mad. Let's hope some more publishers soon get in on the act.

If your personal favourites from Volume One have not returned to these pages, all apologies. Some folks have gone on to greener pastures (check out the section headed BNM Alumni for the latest news). Others are too busy facing their final exams, and have their noses stuck in all sorts of books that aren't even manga. And for many, many more there just simply wasn't room. Don't rule anyone out for next time, though: the doors at BNM towers are always open, and who knows who might walk through them at any time. Plus, there's a host of new names and new faces for you to discover.

In the meantime, wherever you've bought this copy, ask for the growing list of Mammoth comics compilations by name – joining *Best New Manga* on the shelves is *War Comics, Horror Comics* and very soon *Crime Comics*: all of them thick as a brick with tons to read. All respect to the big hairy elephants responsible.

Manga *Jiman*

Volume One brought you past and present winners of the International Manga and Anime Festival (or IMAF): Michiru Morikawa (Grand Prize), Asia Alfasi and Joanna Zhou. Ye Editor was lucky enough to be on the judging panel for IMAF 2006, and is proud as cherry-picking punch to include more winners here in *Best New Manga Volume Two*; first, second and third in the comics category: Laura Howell, Robert Deas and Satanasov respectively, as well as Grand Prize-winner Paul Duffield (who won with his animation).

In June 2007 artists from both volumes One and Two were on show at London's Japanese Embassy, as part of their exhibition Manga *Jiman* (literally meaning 'having pride in manga'), which focused on UK mangaka, and also launched a nationwide competition to discover new talent. The winner gets the trip of a lifetime to Japan, the spiritual home of manga.

This same year also saw at least two other competitions for 'international manga' launched from within Japan. It is hugely significant that the global scene is being acknowledged and welcomed there. And you can be sure the Japanese publishers will be examining closest of all the artists whose manga look the most original and different, rather than those that look the same.

What is Manga?

The debate continues. Here at BNM we'd rather read and enjoy more comic strips than endure articles that endlessly argue over terms. Manga as we know it today originated pretty much with one man – Tezuka Osamu. In 1945, just after the end of the Second World War, Tezuka was influenced by cartoon reels he saw at the cinema, such as *Popeye*, along with the American comic books the occupying forces left behind. He combined these with his own cultural heritage to produce a new hybrid form of comic strip – manga. In the 60-plus intervening years, manga has continued to spread and develop in the hands of many.

One distinguishing feature of manga, under the surface, is the sense of timing or pacing. Manga storytelling allows for flashbacks and cuts between sequences, but in almost any given scene events usually play out in real time. Manga tends to stay in the perpetual ever-present, albeit one wherein time may be made to go faster, or slower, or even both at the same time.

This makes for a more truly immersive reading experience – the reader is right there alongside the featured character, sees all that they see, and feels all that they feel as the result. This serves to strengthen our emotional ties to the characters – we can relate, feel bonded to them, and identify with their struggles, their loves, their hopes and dreams as they experience them right there on the page in front of us. This empathy, this elevated level of psychological insight, is one of the very greatest strengths of manga.

Speaking in the very strictest sense, comics creators living and working outside of Japan cannot make manga. It is largely taken up as a term of convenience and expression of will if not the way. As much as many mangaka would love to, they haven't the opportunity to create manga properly – there simply isn't room. The weekly strip serial publications don't yet exist that would sustain the page counts necessary for such decompressed storytelling. Nor, indeed, is there an eager and demanding readership in the millions to feed. We've gone straight to importing the book compilation formats that collect those same weekly strips together – and it takes many months of hard work to create that many pages.

Until we begin to sell more copies of any originated title, it is difficult for mangaka outside of Japan to find any financial reward for their efforts. Thus, we remain at a level where we perfect our craft in the short story-format – sometimes no more than a blink in manga terms – or bravely flying solo, crafting a longer serial in the hopes that it may one day be collected into its own book or series of books. We are still very much learning the craft, against the odds, and despite unfavourable conditions. All the more remarkable then, the sheer strength and variety of what is being written and drawn, a small taste of which can be sampled in these very pages.

Rising as it did from the atomic ashes of Nagasaki and Hiroshima, the manga format continues to cross-pollinate, West to East and East to West, and to mutate into ever newer forms. Foreign mangaka who purely mimic what is an innately Japanese form of expression are doomed to repetition of tropes and clichés they might never truly encompass, nor fully understand. Far more interesting are those who take up the medium they love and learn from it, yet bring just as much of themselves to the drawing table – whose work shows off their own unique cultural backgrounds and interests; just the same as Tezuka did, once upon a time. That is truly manga.

Manwha...huh?

Produced outside of Japan, principally in China and Korea, manwha is distinct from manga. It halfway resembles a more American comic form and layout – often in colour, more panels per page, and tending towards superheroic distortions, with characters being Hulk and He-Man muscular. This style merges with far Eastern mythic traditions and cosmology to produce high-flying and fist-firing god-hero epic cycles, the sort of thing echoed in *Wushu* cinema by the likes of *Hero* and *Crouching Tiger, Hidden Dragon*. *Dragon Last*, featured in our colour section, wears the influence of manwha on its sleeve... but comes from Bulgaria. Huh?

All the Ladies in the House...

Look through any volume of *Best New Manga,* and one thing you may notice is the proliferation of female heroes – Eve3000, Abigail Cross and Keiko Panda. Not only that, though; at least half of the creators are female (the two are not necessarily connected – Keiko was created by blokes).

Now we didn't plan it that way: we didn't have to try, fill quotas, employ tokenism, or make any sort of special dispensation – that's just the way it is. Half of the folks making the best new manga are female.

The readership can't quite so readily be quantified, but we estimate that the creative community for manga is equally divided between the sexes – 50/50 if not 60/40 in favour of the ladies, which not only matches the statistic for the larger population, but also reflects manga as a truly popular movement – the most people-led medium there is. That's enormously relevant, because the sad fact is there is no other medium that equally represents the female half of the population – not in comics, not in film, music, politics or anything else. That is by far the most significant aspect of the manga phenomenon, and probably one of the least commented on; this aspect alone should mean that manga is here to stay.

Oh, and if you are one of our male readers? That doesn't mean you have to drop the book like a hot potato... Reading *Best New Manga* in public won't make you look girlie: it'll make you look normal.

Live and arrived, this is the twenty-first century folks!

Make More Manga!

Check out the biographical pages for each of our artists and writers, in their own words. Last issue we asked contributors to nominate their likes and dislikes. This time around we're exploring what their ambitions are, both inside and outside of manga. Manga serials are traditionally long form, running into hundreds if not thousands of pages across many volumes. Relatively speaking, all we are able to display here are short stories – tasters, mere samples of what might be possible. Pretty much everyone whose work you'll read here is willing and capable of filling a book as big as this one all by themselves. Hopefully, together, we can soon make that a reality while getting lots more unique and thrilling manga to read into the bargain. We're hoping you'll check out the links to their various websites and give them your further encouragement and support. There's still so much more to read out there, and it's happening now.

Best New Mangaaaaah!

When nearly everything you see, hear, taste, and read these days is moderated, mediated and merchandised, manga is a living and breathing medium of storytelling that's taking things back to the individual act of creation. Rather than the product of some anonymous and shadowy marketing department, these stories are carefully crafted by and for people just like you and me. They are the modern day-myths and legends of our pan-cultural imagination in their purest form.

So step up, join in, come visit the many and varied worlds of manga – you'll never want to go home again.

Enjoy the book!

– ILYA
Manga Wrangler

IVAN SONG Beat Me

'I love to tell stories that involve the readers emotionally. Stories that they can relate to, learn from, cry over or laugh at. That is why I am working towards becoming a full-time manga creator and looking to have my own series published by next year.

'As it's no fun eating only one flavour of ice cream for life, I try to not limit my stories to a single genre. From tragic love to brutal action, as long as it's a tale worth reading, it's one worth telling.

'Drop by my website (like right now!) to read more of my manga and do tell me what you think of them by leaving a comment.' – **Ivan**

www.gadacreations.com/mangada/

2

3

6

What is *Chibi?*

To illustrate their biographical information, we've asked creators to represent themselves with a *chibi*-style portrait. *Chibi*, 'Super Deformed' or 'SD' is a styling unique to manga. This Japanese word literally translates as 'small' or 'kid'.

It is most often used to denote a comedy situation, or perhaps in certain circumstances an extreme emotional outburst – sometimes even within a storyline that is otherwise realistic or serious in tone. The characters are depicted (and often re-imagined) with enlarged heads and short-limbed little bodies, proportions close to those of an infant. Actions, as with their features – whether bawling, laughing, running about or stamping up and down in a rage – are exaggerated for effect. Have a go: picture yourself, a family member, a favourite fictional character, a celebrity or whoever you like, and imagine what they'd look like as a *chibi*. The more ridiculous and stupid they end up looking, the better.

Chibi art: Andi Watson

LAURA HOWELL

The Bizarre Adventures of Gilbert & Sullivan

'Even though I've been a doodler for as long as I can remember, somehow I got sidetracked away from an arty career when I left school. Despite having a perfectly respectable job in publishing, the urge to draw wouldn't go away. Finally, in 2006, I reached a point where I had to go for it or never forgive myself for not trying. Winning IMAF and becoming a professional comic artist since then (I work for *The Beano* – yes, I mostly do comics that aren't manga) is a dream already fulfilled for me. If I had to be greedy and want more, though, I'd like to find a permanent home for Gilbert and Sullivan's 50-odd (and growing) adventures, then travel the world in search of new stories to tell. And also learn to cook the perfect *okonomiyaki*.

'Influences: G&S is probably influenced most by *DiGi Charat* – the mix of cuteness and non-sequiturs blew me away the first time I saw it. I don't read all that much manga these days, but Rumiko Takahashi is an old favourite; I've always found the best humour comes from mixing reality into off-the-wall weirdness, and she's an expert. Of course, Britain has its own rich tradition of quirky humour, W.S. Gilbert himself being a notable lover of the absurd. I'd like to think he'd approve of becoming a manga star and fighting robots.' – **Laura**

www.itsamouse.com/LauraHowell

You can find further bizarre adventures of
Gilbert and Sullivan on pp. 375–6 and 524–6

Another Summer Day

NANA LI Another Summer Day

'**Born in China,** I moved to Sweden very early on. I'm definitely feeling more Swedish or at least international than Chinese, but my background of course has an impact as well. I've been back there every now and then to visit relatives.

'I try to balance my art and studies (technical engineering) – educating myself in what's possible for me, as well as coming to a better understanding of what I want to do in life. When it comes to drawing and manga my greatest ambition is to improve my technical skills, to learn more and experiment. These things take time though and time seems like the last thing I have on my hands right now. I'd love to draw manga for a living of course. I think I have quite a bit to go before then.

'I started drawing manga before I read it. I somehow got my hands on a CLAMP* manga a few years back, before such things were readily available, and the art just dazzled me. I really wanted the ability to draw like that. Certainly, had it not been for manga, I probably wouldn't be drawing as much as I do today.

'I'm a big fan of Masashi Kishimoto's work on *Naruto*.' – **Nana**

* Studio CLAMP is a famously popular all-female mangaka collective from Japan.

SPLASH

YOU'RE GOING
TO BREAK IT,
YOU KNOW.

19

25

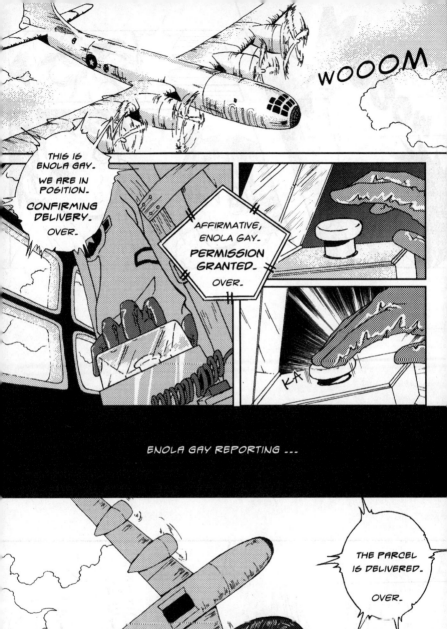

Rural England, 1915

Germany, 1989

Hiroshima, August 6, 1945

ROBERT DEAS November

'**I have one ambition** and that's to make comics for a living. Comics are my passion. Drawing comics is who I am.

'*November* is based on my final university project. It has long been my dream to see it in print and here it is, the first chapter anyway.

'My influences include Masamune Shirow, Katsuhiro Otomo, Frank Miller and the work of a hundred concept artists, especially Ryan Church. I'll never forget the first time I saw *Akira* and how it opened my eyes up to the world of manga and anime*.

'I host my own webcomic, *Instrument of War*, a Sci Fi epic about one man's struggle to save the woman he loves by travelling across space to find her – another title I hope to see in print one day. You cannot underestimate how much deadlines can help to push your work. Since starting my website my work has really improved. No more perfecting every last line and starting again after the fourth page. The minute you have people reading your work you have an obligation to deliver. If it's not perfect, then you deal with it, and make the next page better than the last.

'A spin-off from *Instrument of War*, *Unity Rising* came second in the print comic category at last year's IMAF competition and was the start of this journey, getting my first break into the world of comics.' – **Rob**

www.rdcomicsonline.com
Email: rdcomics@rdcomicsonline.com

---

* Manga and anime are very closely related. Otomo created over 4000 pages of his manga *Akira*, and also directed the feature length animated film version.

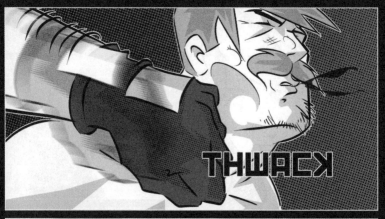

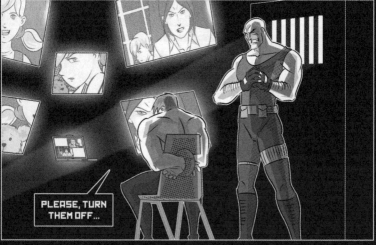

PLEASE, TURN
THEM OFF...

I'M BEGGING YOU.

KƎNYA

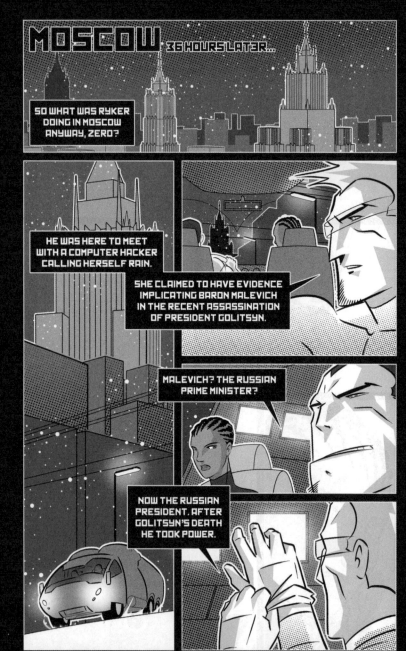

47

WE'RE HERE. THE KREMLIN'S SOUTH WALL, OUR POINT OF ENTRY.

49

52

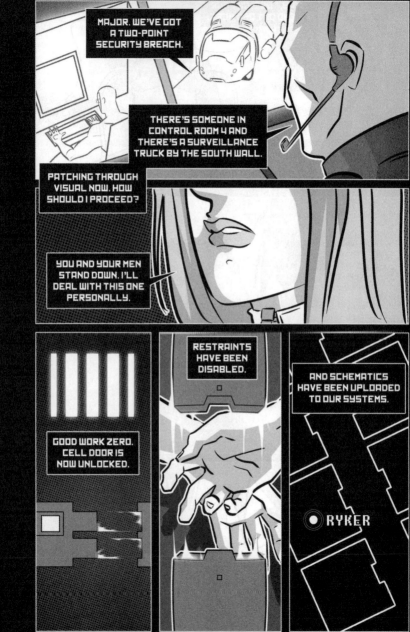

61

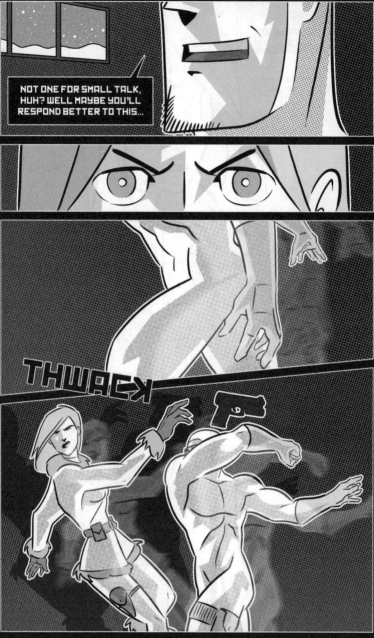

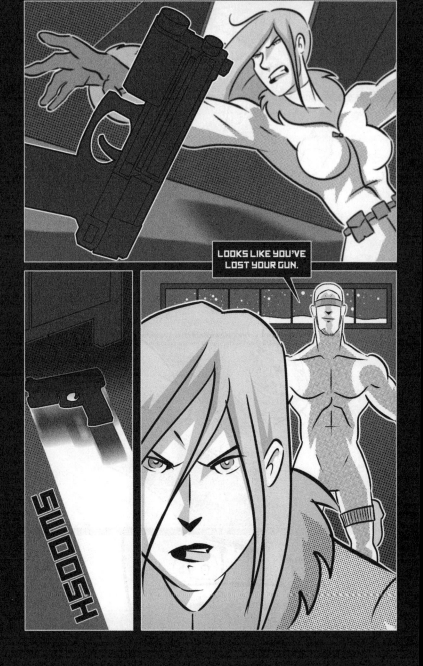

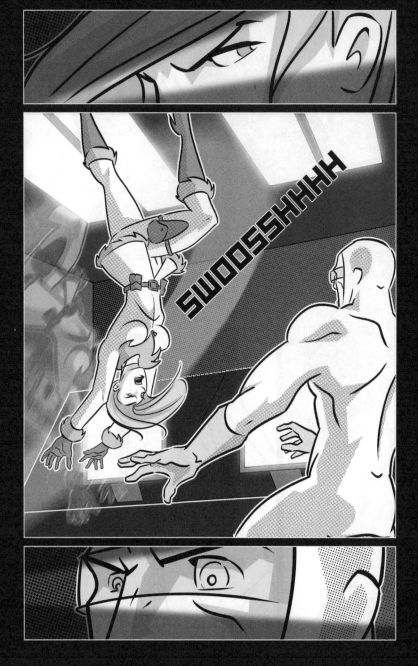

SWOOSSHHHH

64

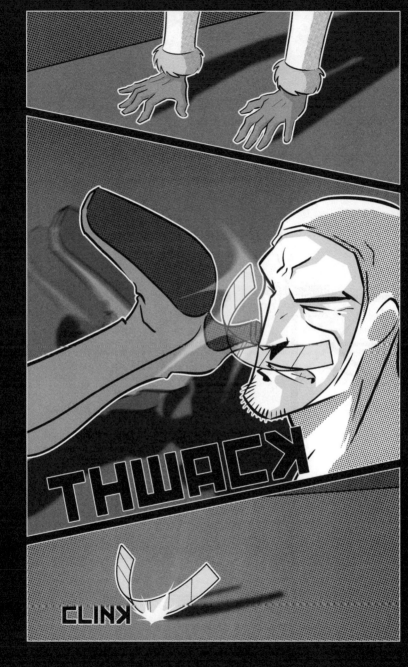

66

71

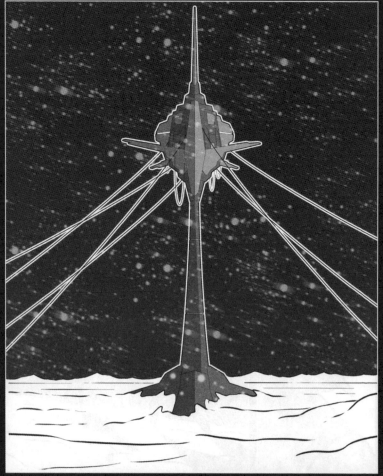

72

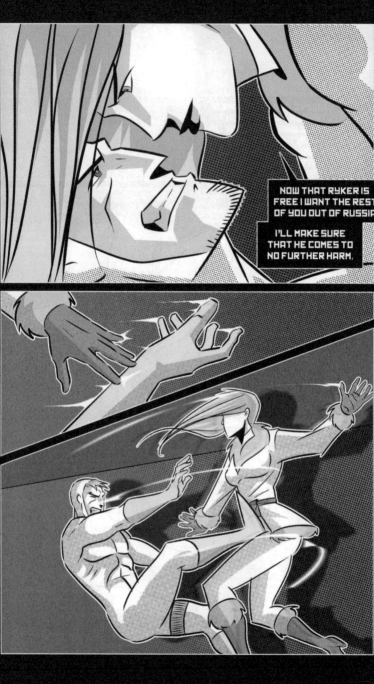

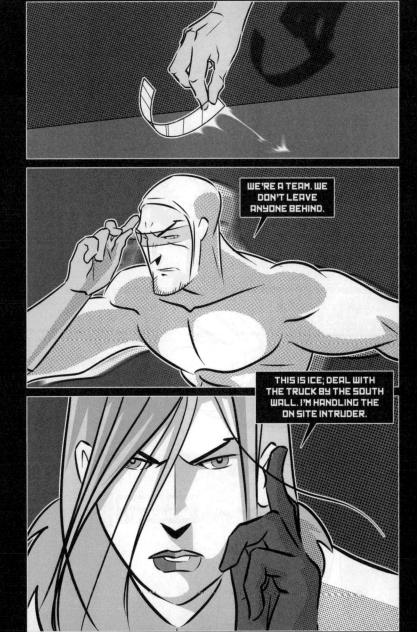

84

86

88

YISHAN LI (art) & SEAN MICHAEL WILSON (story)
Story of Lee

'**I started to draw** manga as a freelance artist when in the first year of university, in 1999. I joined a professional studio, and started to publish in manga magazines in China. In 2003 I came to the UK to study business, but after graduating found it hard to get a job, so drew again. I soon realized it is a far better job to do than sitting in an office all day, so I continue to work full-time as a freelance.

'My dream is in the near future to have at least one of my books sell more than 50,000 copies, and for a bigger dream, I wish one day there is an animation made from my manga and people do cosplay of my characters :)' – **Yishan, now living in Edinburgh**

'**Writer Sean Michael Wilson** suffers from a rare condition known as "the 3Ms" – MAGICK, mad mod MUSIC, and MANGA. We should say comic books, really, but then that spoils the M thing.' – **SMW from Scotland, now living in Japan**

http://sean-michael-wilson.blogspot.com/
www.boychildproductions.co.uk

Here's a possible example of *josei*, a kind of more grown-up form of *shoujo* or girls' comics – as *seinen* is to *shonen*, boys' comics; most of the manga material that's currently translated into English is either *shoujo* or *shonen*, and popularly mistaken as the limits of 'manga style' but of course there is no such thing.

'A lot less idealized and more realistic, yeah,' says US mangaka Niki Smith. 'Not as much fluff and sparkles! *Josei* is typically aimed at women in their twenties.'

See how you like it...

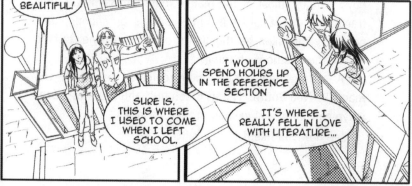

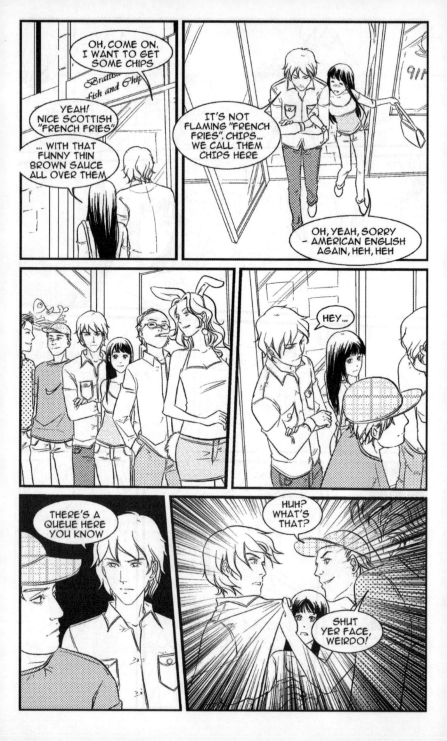

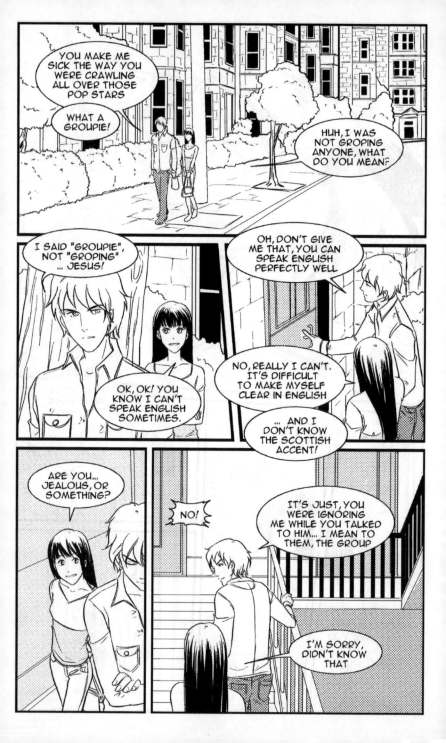

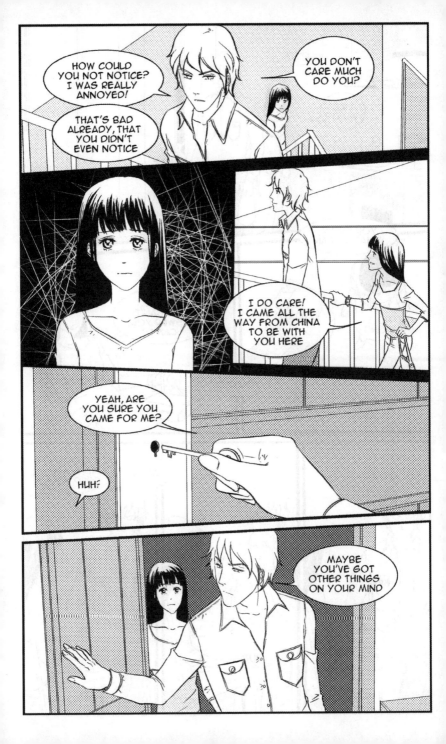

SHARI CHANKHAMMA (art) & FEHED SAID (story)
The Forgotten Incident of San Sabian

Comics – **manga** – have always been my dream, and pretty much are my entire life. Although, finally, I have my works published like I've dreamt of, I still don't feel like I've achieved my goal. There's a lot else I want to achieve; to be more established, more respected and well-known, that sort of thing; but the biggest dream is probably of being allowed to work on a manga adaptation of my favourite author, Neil Gaiman's works.

'I find it hard to think about my other ambitions. The biggest challenge is probably writing a novel, in English, and getting it published – but I have a long, long way to go.' – **Shari**

http://sharii.com

'**I set myself goals** all throughout my life. I have to do this. For the last few years my biggest was to get Shari and myself published in the USA, something we were able to achieve this year with the release of our 200-page graphic novel *The Clarence Principle* (through Slave Labor). We really pushed the boundaries – not just artistically, but also between western comics and manga. It's a rather difficult piece to follow up on.

'After working on this short piece for *Best New Manga*, though, I find myself tackling an idea for a three-volume manga for us to work on, *Maron's Door* – another fantasy piece that delves into the realm of dreams and nightmares, but as always with our own original take on it. My current ambition is to find a publisher for this series.

'Outside of comics, one of my dreams in life is to work on a short film someday. Being such a movie geek, it's only natural I guess. I adore working on comics so much lately, however, that I count myself lucky to be where I am today. Not many people can say that.' – **Fehed**

http://sixkillerbunnies.com
http://www.sweatdrop.com

Story/ Fehed Said
Art/ Shari Chankhamma

124

125

136

HEY THERE,

I JUST WANTED TO COME OVER AND MEET THE MAN RESPONSIBLE FOR ALL THIS.

THIS IS ALL YOUR FAULT ERIC.

ERIC!!

143

I STAY ALIVE...

AS THEY ARE.

159

IN SAN SABIAN.

KAREN RUBINS Tsuchigumo

'Dreams are private myths,
myths are public dreams.'
– Joseph Campbell

'Alongside her sister Anna, Kaz is co-creator and artist of acclaimed UK independent comic series *Dark*, soon to be a graphic novel. She has been drawing comics ever since she can remember, on solo projects and with other writers. Kaz loves to talk about herself in the third person, which maybe explains her fascination with samurai.

'Ahem. It was through Wendy Pini's *Elfquest* that I first got into manga and anime. I grew up in the days of Manga Video*, and misspent my young girlhood watching classic anime such as *Ninja Scroll*, *Tokyo Babylon*, *Battle Angel Alita* and *Akira*. Other major influences include: Hiroaki Samura, Junji Ito, Rumiko Takahashi, and the Hernandez Brothers (*Love and Rockets*).'

'Set in feudal Japan, the story of *Tsuchigumo* is partly based on a myth, but also taken from a dream, the invented character of Kintaro turning out strangely analogous to legend. That's Collective Consciousness for you.

'I have dreamed about crossing Siberia by rail, and taking a trip to Japan. That's also an ambition of mine. Otherwise, to do what I do and do it well!' **– Karen**

www.kazmantra.co.uk
www.darkplace.co.uk
Email: k_rubins@yahoo.com

---

* Yes, one of the first companies to import anime to the West in a big way managed to call itself Manga Video, causing a confusion of categories that persists to this day.

LEGEND HAS IT THAT KINTARO GREW UP IN THE WOODS AROUND ASHIGARA, WITH WILD ANIMALS FOR HIS COMPANIONS.

IT WAS CLAIMED HE POSSESSED INHUMAN ABILITIES, AND WAS ABLE TO SPEAK THE LANGUAGE OF BEASTS AND BIRDS.

RUMOURS ABOUNDED ABOUT HIS SUPERNATURAL PARENTAGE: HIS FATHER WAS A DRAGON, OR HIS MOTHER A MOUNTAIN WITCH.

WHATEVER THE TRUTH OF HIS ORIGINS, AND FOR WHATEVER REASONS, FATE BROUGHT KINTARO INTO THE PRESENCE OF GENERAL MINAMOTO NO YORIMITSU.

YORIMITSU WAS SO IMPRESSED WITH THE MYSTERIOUS BOY THAT HE ASKED KINTARO TO ACCOMPANY HIM BACK TO THE CAPITAL TO BECOME ONE OF HIS PERSONAL RETAINERS.

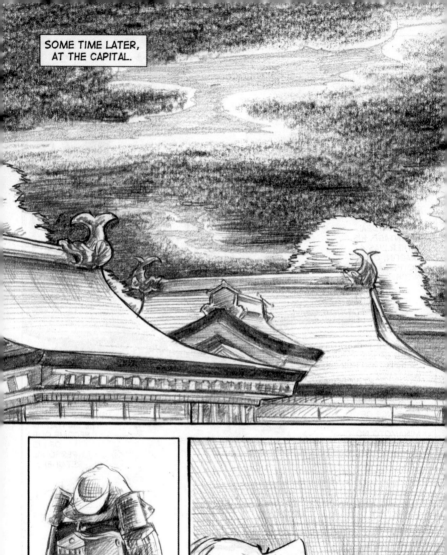

SOME TIME LATER,
AT THE CAPITAL.

FLAP
FLAP

HIDEHARU-SENSEI

WHO ARE YOU MAKING WAR AGAINST?

OH, SO THIS IS ABOUT YORIMITSU. YOU REALLY SHOULD GIVE UP YOUR UNHEALTHY ATTACHMENT TO THAT HUMAN.

HE'S BEEN BITTEN, AND THAT'S IT.

THE DEMON SPIDER, TSUCHIGUMO.

THERE IS A WAY TO SAVE HIM. THE SPIDER WILL RETURN TO FINISH HIM. IF THE DEMON'S SOUL IS DESTROYED, ITS INFLUENCE WILL BE BROKEN.

GOOD EVE, BRAVE WARRIOR.

I CAN SHOW YOU THINGS NO OTHER WOMAN CAN.

I CAN BELIEVE THAT..

...TSUCHIGUMO!

SPFFT

OH? I THINK WE WILL BE SPENDING SOME TIME TOGETHER.

HEH.

I CAN'T LET HER DISTRACT ME. IF I CONCENTRATE I CAN SEE THROUGH THE PHYSICAL INTO THE SPIRIT, LOCATE HER SOUL, AND TAKE IT.

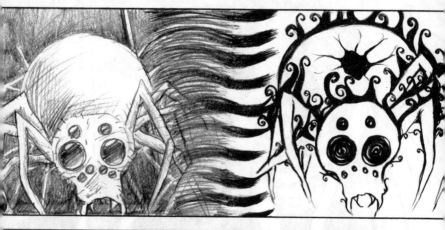

NOW I HAVE YOU.

KINTARO? WHAT ARE YOU DOING HERE?

GUARDING YOU..?

ANNA MERCEDES(lyrics) & RAINBOW BUDDY (art)
Eve3000 (p.188)

'Set in the 26th century, Eve leaves Earth to save humankind, travelling through space to a planet called Nuropa. As Eve, it is my ambition to have the full length-album released along with the story presented as a manga, going on to become a full length-feature anime.' – **Anna**

'Anna is a great singer! And she also creates stories in her lyrics. The album 'Eve3000' is fabulous. It'll be best to listen to the album while you read the manga.' – **Buddy**

OK, you want category confusion? Inspired by both manga and anime, 'Eve3000' was created and composed by American Anna Mercedes as the soundtrack to an imaginary film. The music was written and recorded by Anna and Andy Chatterley in London. While at the IMAF festival Anna met Rainbow Buddy from China, and together they decided to make a manga adaptation of the life and songs of 'Eve3000'.

www.eve3000.com
You can hear some of the music from *Eve3000* on this site.

RAINBOW BUDDY Picnic (p.210)

'I was born in Beijing, China, in 1983. Many of my manga artworks have been published in Chinese magazines, and I've illustrated for lots of novels as well. My influences are Yukiru Sugisaki, Ai Yazawa, Ichiko Ima, and also Rumiko Takahashi. Studio Ghibli's animes are my favourite.

'In China I have lots of fans and they're always supportive of me. Thanks to them, my manga story *Delicious Seasons* can be found in the Chinese magazine *comicfans* every month, and is also published as a book in the USA.

'Right after I finished my MA course in illustration in the UK, I spent three months in London. I loved it there and got to know many of the nicest people. My wish is to make the best manga stories I can, and to show my manga art to people around the world. Also, I'd like to work with brilliant writers. In China, original manga (in Chinese it should be *manhua*) is growing really fast. I hope that more and more Chinese manga artists can be introduced to the global market.

'*Picnic* is a small part of a longer story, which is about adventure and romance. The girl and the bear are going on a great journey together.' – **Buddy**

Rainbow Buddy (aka Ivy Ling), is also the cover artist for this volume of *Best New Manga*.

www.buddy-net.net
www.tokyopop.com/buddy

KATE BROWN
The White Tower (p.228)

'*The White Tower* – a (very, very) short piece about the Princes Edward and Richard imprisoned in the Tower of London – is no more than a few lines of dialogue, as it was the first sequential piece that I've drawn since like 2004 or something. Some of the textures used in the art are photos of stones of the actual Tower. (Fact!)

'Right now I'm working on *A Midsummer Night's Dream* for Manga Shakespeare, to be published early in 2008. I'm also trying to find time to continue pitching projects with my partner Paul Duffield (see page 387). I also sometimes work in Oddbins on Oxford High Street. Sometimes I sleep, too.

'What's my ambition outside of comics? I don't understand the question... although I'm currently eating a tub of ice cream, and I hope to finish that very soon.' – **Kate**

http://danse-macabre.nu
http://kandinsky-prince.deviantart.com
http://comicspace.com/kate

CUBBIE Language (p.233)

'**My biggest ambition in** life would be to earn a lot, become a conservationist under the Cheetah Conservation Fund in Africa, and save the cheetahs! Within comics it's simply to become a manga artist. I won a grant from MSC Malaysia – my country's leading creative multimedia company – to produce and publish a one-shot 190-page comic book entirely by myself. The comic's called *Waterproof*, based on a legendary Malaysian spirit called the "oilyman", whose body is constantly covered in oil. Following that, I hope to team up with a scriptwriter and produce another comic. I also hope that people will start respecting mangaka for their hard work – all that sweat and effort! (Buy the books, not scanlate them! Haha, still, free stuff is good, aint it?)

Cubbie

'Influences: Akira Toriyama (*Dragonball, Dr Slump*), Kaoru Mori (*Emma*), Inoue Takehiko (*Slam Dunk*) and many others!' – **Cubbie**

http://cheetahcub.org
http://cheetahcub.deviantart.com

In the year 2012 NASA's Terrestrial Planet Finder
discovered a planet 116 light years away that was
thought could be an Earth-like planet. It was named
Nuropa. An unmanned exploratory ship was sent in
2032 on a one-way mission to send back data from
the planet. It is the 3rd planet of a twin red dwarf
star system. On reaching the planet after a 580
year journey it sent back data and images received
in 2728.

But by this time the Earth had become a very
different place.

They then began designing the shuttle for the mission
that I will undertake. It will take 214 years to travel
to Nuropa. I will reach the planet in the year 3000
and begin a new human civilization.

It is the hope of the Earth's people that this new
human population will not follow the same course
that has brought about the Earth's sterilization and
pollution, as well as the moral downfall of the people
where technology...

...has overtaken humanity.

The UnholyCreator enslaves the population with illusions.

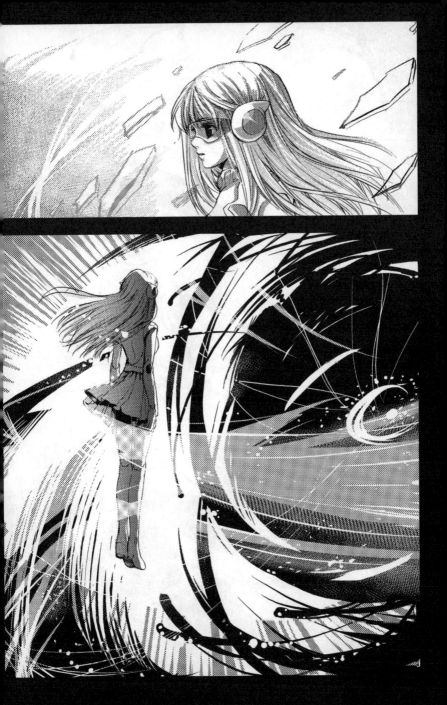

My destiny awaits.

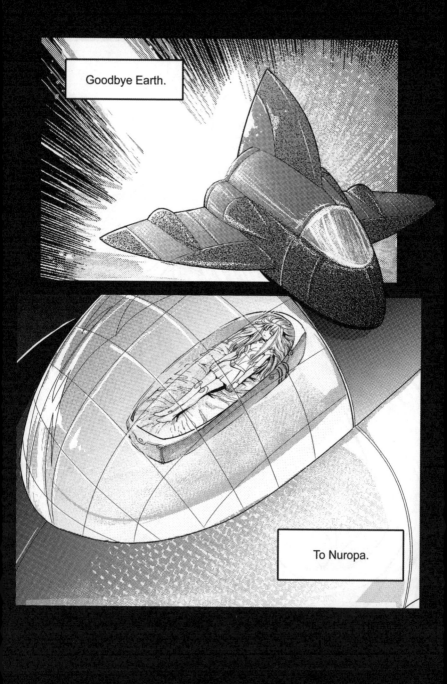

Goodbye Earth.

To Nuropa.

KACHA..

224

225

END

Language

by

Cubbie

It's Her..!

She's here, again...

...gazing at the books...

...while I gaze at her.
She is like a timeless work of art.

The gracefulness, of her hands flipping the pages...

Seeming unmindful of others...

...only adds to her serene aura ...

... and makes me want to know her all the more.

It's a good thing that I came to this library last week.

237

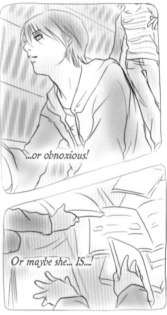

And that's how we first met...

It was our so-called "weaknesses" that brought us together.

Our own Language ~

EVE YAP Images of Crush (p. 245)

'I'm a **Malaysian-born Chinese,** currently working as assistant producer for a 3D animation studio. We make visuals for commercials, corporate videos, and animation series. Drawing and comics have been my hobbies since I was young. My greatest goal in my job is to produce an animation that combines the best of both visuals and storytelling. I made two short films for my university projects: one, *Fall*, won a bronze award in the Singapore Siggraph competition. Another film won best 3D award in China.

'Two of my previous manga short stories were published in a local comic magazine, but it folded before *Images of Crush* could also appear. It's printed here for the first time.' – **Eve**

Hmm. Eve (Yap) should get together with Anna and Ivy (*Eve3000*), and then some enterprising soul should give them lots of money to make their anime feature happen.

http://pinkyee.deviantart.com
Email: eveyap00@gmail.com

PIN-UPS

Karl Wills: *Comic Friend* (p. 241) – Karl Wills (33), a New Zealand-based cartoonist, self-publishes and distributes comics and animation through The Comic Book Factory. He is currently working on a 100-page science fiction comic. *Comic Friend* was a joint effort working with cartoonist-turned film director Andy Conlan. **www.comicbookfactory.net**

Rob Deas: *November* (p. 243) – Here's a version in full colour of the title page to *November* by Rob Deas (see page 39).

Ben Ang: *Agent Liz, Prosthetic Police* (p. 244) – Agent Liz, Prosthetic Police is a character created by Ben Ang (see page 417).

Ben Ang Presents

Agent

LIZ

Prosthetic Police

IMAGES of Crush

WHAT!!! You jerk! How and where the hell d'you get it from?

Wow... slow down. I got it from the class monitor. Quite a reliable source, eh... heheh

Really!?! From the class rep? That dork!? What a shame

So do you want it or not?

Duh ~ you need to ask? Of course I want it! C'mon, gimme... gimme quick!

Alright, stop pestering, I need to search first... Here...0...1...3...

Come in!

HEADM
ROOM

Robert here to report, sir

Hazel's here too...!?

As we all know, Robert here has been taking photos of you without your consent

I have chosen to let Ms. Lee decide whether or not we should report this behaviour to your parents...

Hey! Enjoy sweeping? Serves you right for being such a creep! Hahaha!

Phew… it's fortunate Hazel didn't want to make this a big hoohah. So sweet and considerate… I still get punished for taking photos of Miss Big Mouth, though!

SHAAAH…

Oh ghod… I'm sorry, I didn't mean to…

…!

It's OK

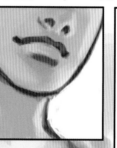

Hazel's been taking photos of ME this whole time?!

Alright, you sinner! You & me better get all this cleaned up before someone else comes over and teases us!

By the way, wanna see my shot of the Headmaster minus his wig?

Haha... really? Boy, do we have something in common...

SATANASOV

DRAGON LAST

ABOUT ME

My name is Daniel, but I am most known as
Satanasov or Boreworm.
I was born in a small town in Bulgaria, where
MANGA was unknown when I started to do it.
That happened in the late
80s when I still was a kid. Since then a lot of
things have changed.
I grew up, got married and became a father
but I've never left behind my dream to
become a mangaka.
All this would never be possible without the
support and understanding of my family.

I dedicate this to my wife Irina and my son
Yantar.

www.satanasov.com

SPECIAL THANKS:
Lettering: **Thomas Mauer**
http://thomasmauer.blogspot.com/
(I will always owe u a beer, man :)

Editor: **ILYA**
the good, old (literally;) one

And all of **YOU**,
who read this and support the manga in all its shapes!

IN THE BEGINNING OF TIME, **DRAGONS** RULED OVER THE WORLD. THEY WERE **MIGHTY** CREATURES, GIFTED WITH INTELLECT AND MAGIC SKILLS. YET DESPITE THEIR INTELLECT, THEY WERE **SELFISH** AND CRUEL...

...WHICH DROVE THEM INTO A **WAR** FOR SUPREMACY.

AND THAT BECAME THE CAUSE OF THEIR **DOWNFALL.**

AND SOON ENOUGH...

...MANKIND DISCOVERED
THAT THE DRAGONS
WERE **NOT** INVINCIBLE.

WHEREUPON A **LONGING** WAS CONCEIVED WITHIN THEIR HEARTS...

...TO BECOME THE **NEW** MASTERS OF THE WORLD.

IT WAS THE BEGINNING OF THE **END** FOR THE DRAGONS.

RAGHASTA, ONE OF THE LAST DRAGONS, IS FIGHTING DESPERATELY FOR HIS LIFE.

EVEN ON HIS OWN, HIS STRENGTH IS ENOUGH TO DESTROY A SMALL ARMY...

265

269

CHI-TAN (KUTSUWADA CHIE)
King of a Miniature Garden

'**Although born** and brought up in Japan, I now live in London, England, member of a group called Umisen-Yamasen, a collective of five Japanese *otaku* illustrators and mangaka. My background is in fine art but Japanese sub-culture, such as manga, anime and computer games has always been one of my biggest influences. Mangaka whose work I love include Yumiko Oshima (*Wata no Kunihoshi* – 'A Star over the Cotton Country'), Fumiko Takano (*Zettai anzen kamisori* – 'Absolute Safety Razor'), Sakae Kusama (*Hatsukoi no Shiryou* – 'Spirit of First Love') and Asumiko Nakamura (*J no Subete* – 'All About J') for their wonderful balance of high-quality art and strong storytelling.

'It's my ambition to have a studio where nobody disturbs me while I create my manga, illustrations, and dolls (usually beautiful male characters involved). I'm also interested in publishing a compilation of short love stories, plus a regular manga magazine, or perhaps manga adaptations of stories and poems by my favourite authors, such as Hyakken Uchida.

'Meantime, I'd most of all like to create good quality *yaoi* / "boys love" comics. My next work is possibly a modern fantasy/horror with neo-*yaoi* twist.' – **Chi-tan (Kutsuwada Chie)**

www.umisen-yamasen.com

my soul

僕は閉じ込められてる。
I'm trapped.

この島に、閉じ込められてるんだ。
I'm trapped on this island.

そろそろお昼の時間。
拓郎が僕を呼びに来る。

It's almost lunch time.
Takuro is calling me.

Hiiragi!!

They don't like waiting, you know that!

拓郎は僕の世話係。
僕の大好きな人。

Takuro's my carer,
my most favorite person.

この島には、僕たちの他にあと4人いる。
大きな屋敷が一軒だけあって、
そこに僕ら6人は住んでいる。

There are four more people on this island.
We, six of us, all live in a huge mansion,
which is the only house on this island.

Stop messing up my hair!

普段は食事は別々にする。
だけど今日みたいに、特別な連絡のある日は別だ。
We usually dine separately, except when they have something to announce.

恵さんはこの家の執事。
そしてこの女の人は雨純さんといって、この家を管理してる人だ。
Key is the butler, and Ms. Uzumi the lady who's in charge of everything in this household.

皆さん、明日から二日間、私と深雪は留守にします。
Listen everyone. Tomorrow, Miyuki and I are going away for two days.

雨純さんの今日のお知らせは、僕を凄くびっくりさせた。
Ms. Uzumi's announcement today surprised me.

柊さん、
口をお閉じなさい。
みっともない。
Hiragi, please close your
mouth. It's unbecoming.

僕はなんだか、
上手くやれなくて。
I'm not coping
very well.

雨純さんは厳しいし、
この人、雨純さんの片腕の
深雪さんは、ちょっと怖い。
Ms. Uzumi's very strict,
and I'm afraid of this lady,
Ms. Miyuki, who is
Ms. Uzumi's assistant.

くす。
Snigger

下品な子。
What a
lowbrow.

深雪さんと庭師の大和さんは仲良しで、
二人で僕に意地悪なことを言う。
She and Yamato,
who's a gardener of this mansion,
are very close. And they
say nasty things about me.

結局僕は、拓郎以外の人には馴染めなくて、

After all, I can't get on with
other people,

拓郎さえいれば、他に誰も必要なくて、

and the only person I need is Takuro.

気にするなよ。

Don't take any notice.

明日になれば、拓郎としばらく二人きりになれる。

Come tomorrow, there's only him and me.

恵さんとはもともとつきあいはないし、
きっとずっと本館で仕事だろうし。

We usually don't mix with Key, and
he will be working at the main building
anyway.

誰も僕たちの邪魔をしない。
早く明日になればいいのに。

Nobody will disturb us.
I can't wait for tomorrow.

僕らが住む、この島唯一のお屋敷は、
普段雨純さんや深雪さんや恵さんが
仕事をしている洋風の本館と、

The place where we live (there is only
one household on this island)
consists of a European-style main
building, where Ms. Uzumi,
Ms. Miyuki and Key work...

一年前から僕と拓郎が住んでいる、
和風の離れとでできている。

...and a Japanese-style detached
house, where Takuro and I have
been living for about a year.

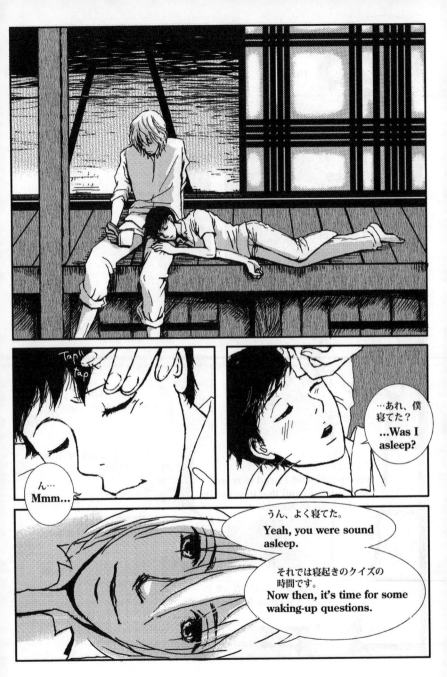

283

拓郎のことだけは、
絶対忘れない。
I'll never ever forget about you.

拓郎が僕の世界の全てだった。
**Takuro is the centre of
my universe.**

二人きりでいられるのが
嬉しくて、楽しくて、
Because I am so happy
to be alone with him,
and it is so much fun,

3日間なんてあっという間に過ぎた。
The three days pass so quickly.

気がつけばもう、
明日には雨純さんも深雪さんも大和さんも
帰ってきてしまう。
I am suddenly aware that
Ms. Uzumi, Ms. Miyuki and Yamato
are coming back tomorrow.

二人だけで過ごせる、
最後の静かな夜。
Tonight is the last night
we can spend on our own.

…柊。
…Hiragi.

うん？
Yes?

それ終わったら、
ちょっとこっちにおいで。
Will you come inside
when it's finished?

わかった。
ちょっと待ってね。
Yeah, sure.
Won't be long.

拓郎？
Takuro?

柊、
大事な話があるんだ。
Hiragi,
I have something very
important to tell you.

明日、雨純さん達が帰ってくるまでに、
お前に話しておかないと。
...Something I must tell you
before Ms. Uzumi and the others
come back tomorrow.

俺がこれから言うことを良く聞いて。
いいね、柊。
Listen carefully to what I'm going
to say, alright?

288

…これが、
お前がこの島に連れてこられた
理由だよ。
**…That's why you were
brought here.**

だって、療養だって！
**No! This is a
part of my
rehabilitation!**

父さんと、
母さんは…、
**My parents
said...**

療養だっ…って…。
**it would be...
good for...me...**

…柊…。落ち着いて聞いてくれ。
…Hiragi, calm down and listen.

う〜…
Umm...

いいか、紅様は近いうちにお世継ぎを
もうけなくてはならない。秘密裏に、だ。
**Soon, Lady Kurenai has to conceive,
and give birth to her successor.
It has to be done discreetly.**

選ばれたのはお前なんだ。
お前が必要なんだ。
**You were chosen.
She needs you.**

291

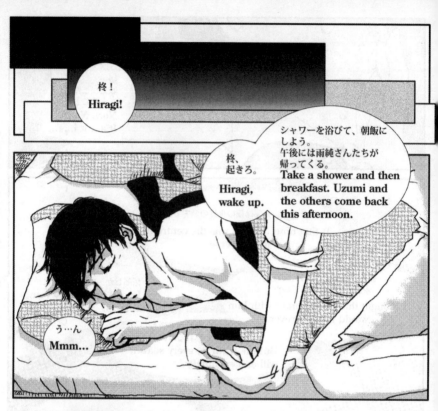

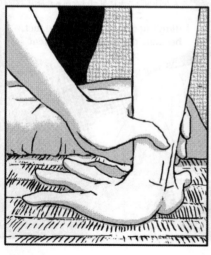

拓郎もいっしょにいて。
ずっと。

**Be with me, Takuro.
Forever...**

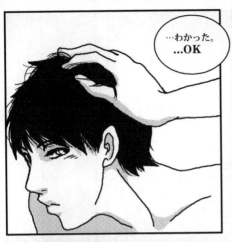

…わかった。
...OK

わかったから、ほら、起きろ！
I said OK, so now get up!

朝飯の用意するから！
I'll prepare breakfast!

わかったって、本当に？拓郎…。
Takuro... Is it really OK?

僕たちはたいした会話もせず、朝ご飯を食べて、
We have breakfast without much conversation,

そして、雨純さん達からの連絡を待った。
Then we just wait for Ms.Uzumi to call us.

297

風邪ひくぞ。
Don't catch cold.

ありがとう。
Thank you...

夜になって、やっと雨はやんだが、母屋から連絡はなかった。
When night falls, it stops raining.
But we haven't heard from them.

今年の蛍はすごいな。
There are many more fireflies this year.

301

302

夜中に突然目が覚めた。
今日連絡はなかったけど、
その、紅という子は、もうこの島に
来てる。そんな気がした。
I suddenly wake up
in the middle of the night.
We have heard no news about
her, but I can feel the girl,
Kurenai, is already on this island.

Mmm…

会いに行かなくちゃ。
手遅れになる前に。
I must meet her.
Before it's too late.

そしてちゃんと言わなきゃ。
And I have to tell her
honestly,

僕は…、
that I...

僕はやっぱり…。
I... can't really...

本館は広くて暗いから、
夜に来るのはちょっと苦手だ。
**The main building is huge and dark,
so I don't like coming here at night.**

でも、この館のどこかに、
彼女はきっといる。
**But she must be here,
in one of these rooms.**

あの部屋、
灯りがついてる…。
**That room…
the light's on…**

初めて会った僕の婚約者は、
My fiancée I meet
for the first time,

予想に反して、よくしゃべり、
よく笑う、無邪気な子供のような人だった。
Contrary to my expectation,
She chats and laughs a lot,
like an innocent child.

ただ、背中に、
However,
on her back,

309

背中に、不思議な、でもとても美しい、
鱗のようなものがある以外、いたって普通の少女だった。

On her back, there is something unusual,
yet beautiful, "...scale like things".
Apart from that, she is just an ordinary girl.

もう出るから！
I'll finish my bath!

まだ帰っちゃ駄目よ。
Please don't leave yet.

あ…
Er...

なあに？
What's the matter?

や、な、なんでも
ない…。
N-No, nothing...

ぼ、僕、何を言おうとしたんだ、
彼女は気にしてるだろうに…。
She must be nervous
about what I was about
to say...

…

この背中？
Is it about my back?

やっぱり気になるよね？
You don't mind, do you?

彼女はすごく嬉しそうに、僕に向かって微笑んだ。
She smiles for me, so very happy.

僕は本当に綺麗だと思ったんだ
ただ慰めようとしたわけじゃないんだ
I really thought it was beautiful.
I didn't just say so to comfort her.

せ、背中、
Your back...

さ、触ってもいい？
Ca-can I touch it?

あ！ご、ごめん！
ぼ、僕、変なこと
言った！
Oh! So-sorry!
I said something
silly!

314

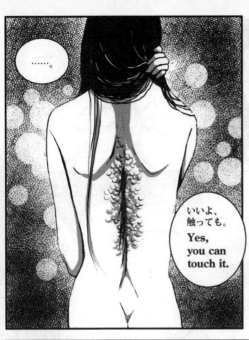

......。

いいよ、
触っても。
**Yes,
you can
touch it.**

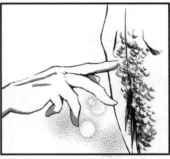

あっ…
Oh...

ちくっ
prick!

痛っ…
Ouch...

だ、大丈夫？
Are you alright?

血の、契約…。
A contract of blood...

316

そして彼女は、唖然とする僕を尻目に、
お気に入りのぬいぐるみのこと、
好きなお菓子のこと、そんな話をさんざん僕に
聞かせた。
She just ignored my astonishment and started
telling me about many things, like her favorite
dolls and sweets.

明日の夜も
遊びに来てね。
Please visit me
again tomorrow
night.

今夜見たいにこっそりと、
誰にもみつかっちゃ駄目。
Come secretly like you
did tonight.
Don't let anybody
catch you.

私たちが会ってる事は、
誰にも秘密だよ。
Tell nobody that
we're meeting.

そう言って、僕らは別れた。
Then I left her room.

結局僕は、彼女に言いたかった事も
なにも言えなかったけど、
After all, I was not able to tell
her what I had wanted to
tell her.

でも…
But...

319

拓郎にも、
Takuro...

言えない秘密…
Not even Takuro
should know
our secret...

321

柊は、これから一生
私のもの……。
From now on,
Hiragi's mine forever...

ごめん…。
Sorry...

あ、だ、大丈夫
だから…。
Er, I'm fine...
so...

そ、それより、
今日はどんな予定?
By the way,
what's the plan for today?

柊、お前…。
Hiragi, you're...

？

なんでもない。
Nothing.

今日な、
Well, today,

母屋で話があるって、さっき連絡があった。
I'm asked to attend a meeting at the main building.

婚約者のことかな？
Is it about my fiancée?

うん、多分な…。
Yeah, probably...

すごく、いいこだった…。
She was a really nice girl...

生懸命人形の話とかしちゃって、
Talked about her dolls with a passion,

もっと話したいな…。
I want to talk to her more...

婚約が嫌じゃないなんて…。
Do I seem not to mind getting engaged?

そんなこと、ない…。
...When I do?

今夜の拓郎は
少し変だった…。
いつもより、もっと、
ずっと…。
Takuro was strange tonight.
He was more...

...

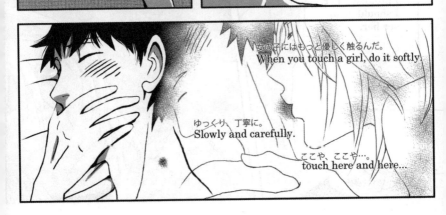

女の子にはもっと優しく触るんだ。
When you touch a girl, do it softly.

ゆっくり、丁寧に。
Slowly and carefully.

ここや、ここや…。
touch here and here...

329

330

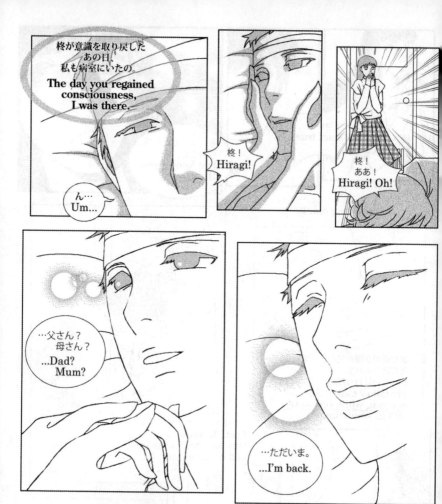

紅…。
Kurenai…

私を迎えに来てくれるって、
勝手に信じてた…。
**...I selfishly believed that
you would come to take me.**

人に、こんな風に望まれる事など
今までなかった。
**For me, this is the first time
in my life I've been wanted
so much by someone else.**

紅。
Kurenai

僕はこの時、人に必要とされる快感を
確かに味わってしまったのだ。
**Now I definitely know the sweet taste
of being needed by another.**

337

338

僕には、拓郎が必要なんだ。
I really need you,
Takuro...

それでは、お二人の出会いと、
柊さんのお誕生日を祝して、乾杯！
Well then, let's raise a toast to
this blissful union and to
Hiragi's birthday!

バルコニーに出ない？
Shall we go out on the balcony?

341

あの…
Listen…

よく考えてみたんだけど、
やっぱり拓郎は特別なんだ。
I've been thinking…
Takuro is special
to me.

僕には彼が必要で…
I need him…

でも君のことは、
何故かずっと知ってるような
気がして…、
As for you, I feel as if
I've known you for
a long time…

うまく言えないけど、
It's hard to explain,
but…

342

343

僕と拓郎の関係は変わらぬまま、紅は頻繁に僕らを訪ねてくるようになった。
The relationship between me and Takuro does not change, but Kurenai starts to visit with us very often.

柊、拓郎さん、おはよう！
Hiragi, Takuro-san Good morning!

なにこれ？
What's this?

うわ！
Wow!

みて みて！！
Look!

紅の明るさと、
With Kurenai's cheerful disposition...

お前の金魚姫は元気だな。
Your goldfish princess is such a cheerful girl.

拓郎の僕らを見守る視線は、
...and Takuro's role as our guardian...

いつしか3人の間に、不思議な均衡をもたらしていた。
...a strange balance forms between us.

秋が深まるにつれ、拓郎は頻繁に母屋から呼び出されるようになり、
When Autumn deepens,
Takuro is frequently summoned to the main building.

僕と紅は
二人きりになることも
珍しくなかった。
I am left alone with Kurenai
quite often.

拓郎としていた
僕の記憶力のリハビリも、

As for the memory checking
test I did with Takuro for
my rehabilitation...

今では、紅とする時
のほうが多かった。

Now I do it
with her .

じゃ次はね、
私の最初のペットの
名前は？

OK next is...
what was my first
pet's name?

えーと、猫のモモ！
Well,
Momo the cat!

正解！
Correct!

…拓郎、遅いね。
...Takuro's late.

葉っぱが…。
A leaf...

350

352

紅様と共に生きるというのは、常に最悪の事態を覚悟していくということ。
If you are to be with her, you must always be prepared for the worst case scenario.

柊さんには、今夜からこちらに泊まり込んでいただきます。
I order you to stay by her beside to look after her.

しばらくは離れには戻れませんから、準備してらして。よろしいわね？
You might not be able to go back to your room for a while, so pack accordingly. Understand?

柊！
Hiragi!

うん、あんまり…。
Not well...

手伝うよ。
I'll help you.

紅様のお加減は？
How is she?

泊まり込むから,荷物を…。
I need to pack an overnight bag...

357

拓郎！
Takuro!

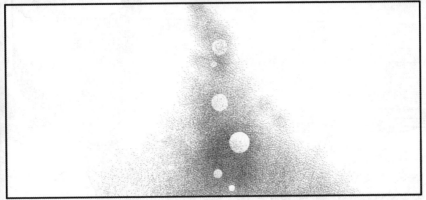

拓郎が去って、5年の月日が流れた。
Five years have passed after Takuro left.

今日は天気は良いけど、
ちょっと寒いね。
**It's a beautiful
day today,
but a bit chilly,
isn't it?**

おはよう、紅。
Hi, Kurenai.

365

366

367

拓郎…？
Takuro...?

覚えててくれたんだ。
You remember me.

あ、あたりまえじゃないか…！
O-of course I do...!

「柊、いつかきっと
拓郎さんに会える日がくるわ。」
"Hiragi, I swear that
you will see him again."

「だからそれまで、
彼の事忘れちゃだめよ。」
"So don't forget him."

…紅はよく僕にそう言ってくれた。
そして、皆で一緒にこの島に住める日を、
いつもいつも夢をみてた。

Kurenai often told me so,
and talked about her dream of all of us living
together on this island.

「私とあなたとこの子、そして拓郎さん。
いつか皆でピクニックしましょう、この丘で、この木の下で。
約束よ、柊」
"Me, you, our baby and him,
let's have a picnic one day under the tree on the hill.
Promise me, Hiragi,"

「約束よ。」
"Promise me."

End

372

What is *Yaoi?*

Yaoi **is a genre** fairly unique to manga, taking male-to-male relationships as its central subject: unusually perhaps, it tends to be by female creators, and caters for a largely female readership.*
Even among mainstream publishers – *yaoi* such as DC Comics with their CMX imprint –*yaoi* has caught on outside of Japan.

Kutsuwada Chie is a founding member of the UK's own artists' collective, Umisen-Yamasen, and writer and artist of *King of a Miniature Garden* (a *yaoi* included in this very volume). In this short interview, she explains her take on *yaoi* appeal: just what is it that makes girls want to tell stories about boys kissing?

CHIE: I talked about the word *yaoi* with Yuki [fellow Umisen-Yamasen member], and we noticed that 'boys love' (or 'BL') is the term much more commonly used nowadays to describe these kind of comics. But perhaps *yaoi* sounds catchier to non-Japanese speakers…

ILYA: I am curious. What is the appeal for girls, do you think, of 'boys love' stories?

CHIE: I think 'boys love' stories have some kind of fantasy factor. The usual love story of girls and boys is close to reality, and some girls might think that that kind of thing will never happen for them. However, for those girls, 'boys love' stories still have a power to make them believe in strong, unconditional love, since 'boys love' stories are nothing like their lives. That's why I believe 'boys love' stories work as fantasy.

ILYA: I agree about fantasy – really, a part of the point of fantasy is that it will never happen (for the fantasist, at least).

CHIE: In most of the 'boys love' stories, the main characters do not initially identify themselves as being gay (some of them are, but at least one is usually heterosexual). So there is almost always the description of the main character's anguish such as, 'Why do I like him? He is a man!' They overcome this anguish and conclude

*Yes, that's right. All the ladies in the house say '*yaoi*'!

373

by thinking, 'It doesn't matter that he is a man, I like him. For him I can be gay or whatever!' Unconditional love, don't you think?

ILYA: And sometimes it's also perhaps unrequited? Although in most of the stories I have read, the protagonist always gets his man! And that is fantasy!

CHIE: That's so right. Today there seems to be no such thing as unrequited or unconditional love, like in *Romeo and Juliet*. Everything about relationships seems to get more and more casual. But some girls think romance is not that casual. They think and fantasize that there is still romance, but it takes place in a *yaoi* world.

ILYA: Do stories of 'boys love' have any male readers/creators in Japan (gay or not), or is that something different?

CHIE: I've heard there are some boys who read 'boys love' stories. They are both gay and straight as well. I've heard that some gay men think 'boys love' stories for girls are too unreal. As far as I know, there are very few male creators of 'boys love' stories and from my point of view, their work looks something between 'boys love' stories for girls and comics for gay men.

Yes, there are also comics for gay men. I haven't read many, but they seem to have more muscles, and a drawing style similar to comics for men, not to girls' comics. I think there's also a gender issue, which is why *yaoi* is so popular. I think in some *yaoi* fans' dark side there might be some kind of desire to have power and conquer men as some men do to women.

I discussed the relationship between society and *otaku* (obsessive fans) in my BA and MA dissertations, so I like thinking about those kinds of things. I could talk about it forever, so I'll stop now.

ILYA: OK. Thanks very much for your insights, Chie.

SOFIA FALKENHEM A Walk in the Woods

'**Someday, I will own** a greenhouse. Otherwise, well, we'll see what happens.

'My big ambition within comics is to tell stories that convey a specific mood or feeling, and to continue exploring how the storytelling within this medium works. I never want to do just one thing, so I prefer continuing as now, working on children's books, comics, graphic art...

'Right now I am working on a, well, it's kind of a sequel to my "fox spirit" mini-comic, and trying out different things with *Instant Noodles* (see *BNM Volume One*), taking it in another direction than first intended. I also have a collection of short stories in mind, so if I just have the time...

'I'm tired of talking about influences – I prefer looking forward – but good storytellers, be it in manga or other comics, and anyone who can use their ink in an interesting way. And, as always, good music and what I see on other artists' desks.' – **Sofia**

www.sofiafalkenhem.com

fin
5-6-06

PAUL DUFFIELD Sojourn

'**As an illustrator I** grew up reading manga (by Jiro Taniguchi, Taiyo Matsumoto, Erica Sakurazawa, Miou Takaya and Maki Kusumoto) and watching anime (by Tatsuyuki Tanaka, Koji Morimoto and Hayao Miyazaki). I studied animation and illustration at Kingston University, discovering how much hard work animation and comics are, and exactly how much there is still to learn... a lot. I had the fortune to win two awards: first place in Tokyopop's first UK Rising Stars of Manga competition, and also grand prize at the 2006 International Manga and Anime Festival (IMAF) for my animated short, *Rolighed*.

'My aspirations are absurdly grand and quite vague – mainly to conquer the world using comics and animation, and to direct an animated feature or series at some point. I would love to see some of my collaborative projects with Kate Brown published. For now though, I'm finishing off an adaptation of *The Tempest* for SelfMadeHero's Manga Shakespeare series.' – **Paul**

www.spoonbard.com
www.spoonbard.deviantart.com
www.comicspace.com/spoonbard

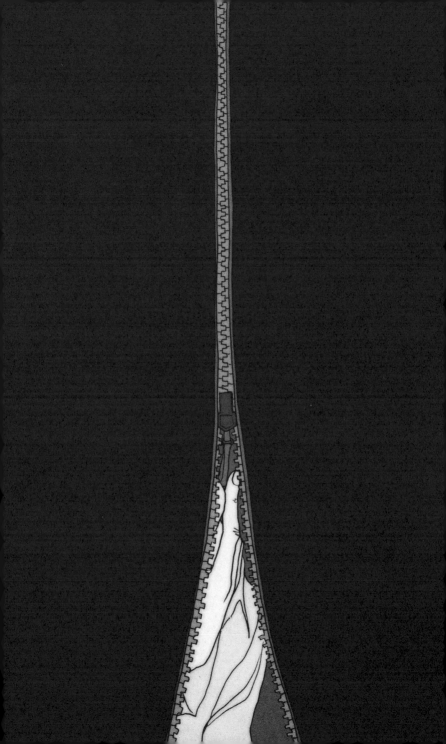

END

Two Alike

Niki Smith

NIKI SMITH Two Alike

'Though still a student and barely 21, Niki Smith is more than ready to jump head first into making comics for a living. She is currently a drawing major at the Cleveland Institute of Art, in Ohio, USA, and studies German on the side... depending on where the winds take her, she may end up needing it!

'Niki's favourite comic artists often work in a *josei* style, but she allows her own style to flex and fit whichever story she's currently working on. She loves personal narratives and quiet scenes, and is currently in the process of pitching a three-volume series.' – **Niki**

www.niki-smith.com

I am young...

but my presence is a default in the minds of most.

I have forced the world to adapt...

conquering and shaping the land with complete disregard for everything that had been there before.

Those who could not adapt have hidden themselves away where my hand has not yet left its touch...

but I am persistent in my own way, and there is little still hidden from me.

Those who could not escape the effect I have had on the land have died,

and I have led to the extinction of many.

My actions have not been malicious...

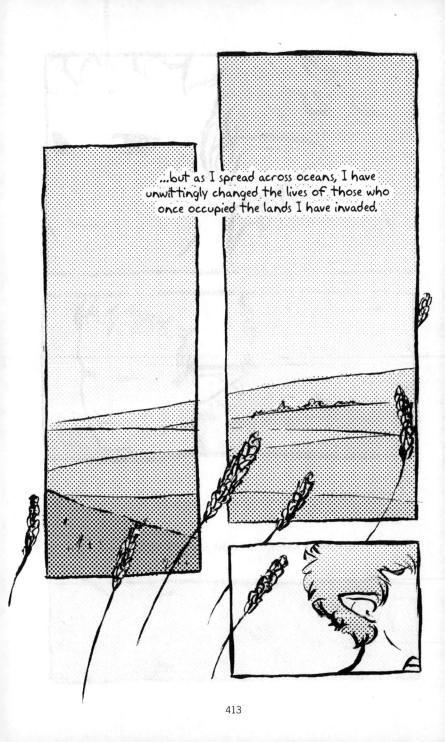

...but as I spread across oceans, I have unwittingly changed the lives of those who once occupied the lands I have invaded.

I am young...

but most cannot imagine a world without me.

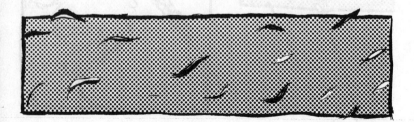

STRUM

for every action, there is a reaction.

by Ben Ang

BEN ANG Strum

'**A freelance illustratorw/designer** from sunny Singapore, I spent all my pocket money on *X-Men* and *Dragonball* comics! When I was 15 an encouraging email from then Assistant Editor of *X-Men*, Jason Liebig, changed my view of comics as a career. I realized this is what I want to do for a living.

'Inspired by the art of Terry Dodson, Joshua Middleton, Bruce Timm, Adam Hughes and Akira Toriyama, I'm currently working on a few comic ideas and will put them online when the time is right. My ambition is to have my own ongoing comic series, and go for sushi buffets everyday!

'With *Strum* I wanted to tell a tale about how everyone affects one another. Like the strumming of a guitar, every chord affects another: for every action, there is a reaction. Special thanks are due to Alex Vasteel.' – **Ben**

http://xplixit.deviantart.com
Email: freelance.ben@gmail.com

418

419

421

423

424

425

431

432

433

434

436

437

438

MR. DODSON?

441

442

445

447

448

the end

CROSS

JASON DENNIS (art) & JOHN A. SHORT (story)
Cross – You Only Die Twice

'**An illustrator with a** Fine Art degree, my first published work was the third part of *Devilchild* and I'm currently layout artist (working with John McCrea) for a comic called *The 99*. Generally I prefer super hero-oriented stuff, action-packed adventure, but I try to use the pacing and panel arrangements of manga. Influences would be Wing Shing Ma, Kenichi Sonoda, anything from Jademan Comics – *Iron Marshal*, *Storm Riders*, that sort of thing (manwha). I'd love to concept-design a movie for a popular super hero character, or completely redesign Alan Moore's abandoned comic *Big Numbers*.' – **Jason**

'**As a Brit, comics,** the *Carry On* films and *Doctor Who* are some of my favourite things, while pet hates include sport, politicians and cultural snobbery. Manga and anime influences might be anything from *Barefoot Gen,* through to *Crying Freeman* and *Marine Boy*, and otherwise Herge (creator of *Tintin*), Dennis Potter and John Woo! You might remember me from my comic *Armageddon Patrol*.

'I'd love to do more with central character Abigail Cross as we are only scratching the surface of her peculiar world here – a pinch of *James Bond*, a slice of *The Vicar of Dibley*, a smattering of *The Boys from Brazil* and a big wodge of *Night of the Living Dead*! In 20 rip-roaring action pages there just isn't time to go into her background, and there is more to her... much more.' – **John**

www.alchemytexts.com
Email: johnashort@hotmail.com

459

463

465

MITZ (art) & JASON COBLEY (story)
Samurai Commander Keiko Panda in Reach for the Sky!

'**Well, I live in** a box-flat in Leicester (UK) with my rats for company (it's true!). Since kicking my online gaming addiction, I fit comics in whenever I can.

'My main ambition in life is to make a living from illustration. As for the direction in comics I'd like to pursue – just good, entertaining stories, usually featuring cute girls. I've been self-publishing for years in various formats, and am currently embarking on an ongoing full-colour downloadable comic, *Joan of Rq* (which is, uh, Joan of Arc in space).

'I'm not a huge manga fan, but like the *Love Hina* books, *Azumanga Diaoh*, *Yotsuba* and *FLCL*. Influences on my work include western creators like Alan Davis, Frank Quitely and old-school pioneers like Alphonse Mucha, who had an early impact back when I was a wee teen.' – **Mitz**

Current work, doodles, comics and pictures of rude things can be found at **www.goonpatrol.com**

'**The *Bulldog and Panda*** manga, anime and toy lines will one day make me very happy. Until then I am content with my current project, a graphic novel adaptation of *Frankenstein* for Classical Comics. A publisher for my collection of modernized international *Folk Tales* should also be announced soon.

'My ambition is to secure a publisher for *Meta-Physix*, an epic tale of metaphysical metamorphosing robots, and also *Driftwood*, a graphic novel about the healing power of dreams. These are both collaborations with famed *Transformers* artist Andrew Wildman. And then there's the sequel to *Bulldog: Empire* (see *Best New Manga Volume One*) where Winston Bulldog tangles with kung fu country vicars, the scheming Women's Institute, and Britain's own ecosystem.

'The biggest inspiration for Keiko is *Ranma*. For myself as a writer, influences include everyone from Haruki Murakami, to Kurt Vonnegut and John Wagner. My greatest ambition is to be mentioned as someone else's influence – so long as it isn't a serial killer!' – **Jason**

www.jasoncobley.blogspot.com
www.classicalcomics.com
www.wild-ideas.co.uk/pubs.html

You can catch the further thrilling adventures of Samurai Commander Keiko Panda in Volume One of *The Mammoth Book of Best New Manga* (and she is the cover star). Ask for it by name at your local bookstore.
Art: Neill Cameron.

481

YOU HAVE BEEN SPENDING TOO LONG WITH CAPTAIN BULLDOG, BRITTANY. SHE IS EMINENT IN CULINARY CIRCLES, SO SHE HAS BEEN SELECTED TO CATER FOR THE INAUGURAL BANQUET OF THE ASTRAL SKY SPAN TOWER. I AM TO ESCORT HER.

HM. NOT THAT I DON'T APPRECIATE BEING ASKED ALONG, BUT I'M NOT BIG ON THIS DIPLOMATIC STUFF. WHY NOT THE CAPTAIN?

THIS EVENT IS UNIQUE IN THAT IT EXCLUDES MEN.

IF IT'S ALL KNITTING PATTERNS AND TUPPERWARE, I'M LEAVING.

I BELIEVE THERE MAY BE JAM MAKING AND FLOWER ARRANGING INVOLVED, BUT YOU CAN ASK HER YOURSELF. THE ENTOURAGE IS ARRIVING.

483

485

486

487

488

489

490

491

492

493

495

496

501

502

503

505

506

507

END...?

Never Forget

BY MUSTASHRIK MAHBUB

MUSTASHRIK MAHBUB Never Forget

'**I am a dreamer** creating visuals, looking at the stars. I love to work with people, I love to learn about the world, honey-roasting cashew nuts. I let my brush twirl. I am a storyteller.

'As an artist, I'm always striving to push and progress in my field of work, looking to learn and take part in this wonderfully expressive career. I absorb everything around me and it sparks a light within, to conceptualize an idea. With my pen and brush in hand, I wish to create visuals for all to see and share with me.

'I am drawn to one thing more than any, and that is people: without them there would not be a world, if a life at all. This story is for everyone I have ever known, everyone I am still to meet, and all those I will never know. Thank you.'– **Mustashrik**

www.mustashrik.blogspot.com
Email: mustashrik@hotmail.com

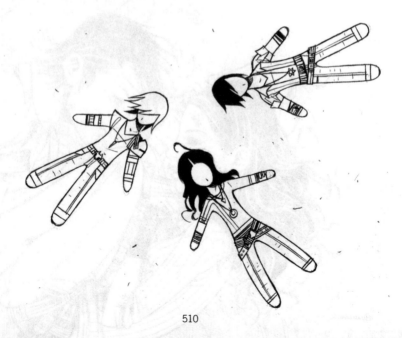

514

518

522

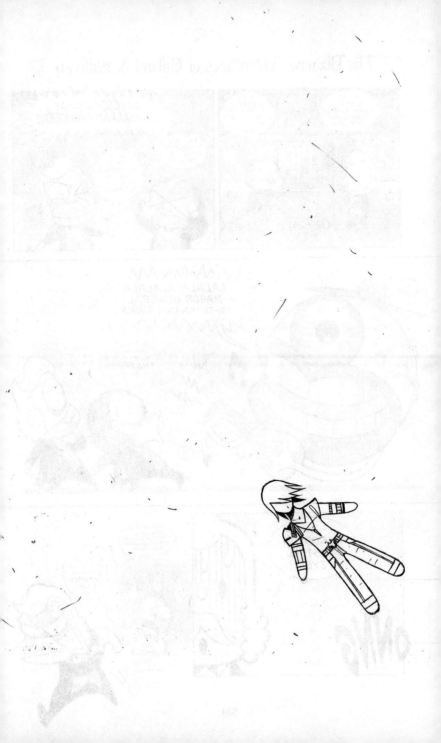

The Bizarre Adventures of Gilbert & Sullivan

524

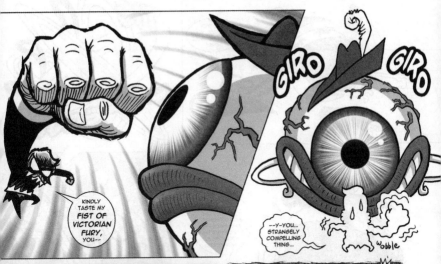

525

BNM ALUMNI

Here's a list of who's doing what since *Best New Manga Volume One* was released in October 2006.

Michiru Morikawa, *Advent* and *Mid-night Transformation* – Michiru has been approached to prepare an as yet unspecified project by Fanfare/ Ponent Mon, a UK/French/Japanese company who originate and publish many excellent manga. Check out their existing range of titles.

Asia Alfasi, *JinNarration* – Asia's story in Volume One featured a Muslim heroine in a traditional *hijab*, a manga first that caused a furore of excitement. She's since exhibited her work throughout Piccadilly Circus underground station, and secured a two-book deal with Bloomsbury for her autobiographical graphic novel, *Ewa*. Asia's cross-cultural experience informs both life and work, for which she finds her perfect match in the hybridized forms of manga.

We have hopes of her returning to these pages in Volume Three.

Kate Brown, *Station* – Kate returns here in full colour (*see The White Tower* on page 228. She is also adapting *A Midsummer Night's Dream* for SelfMadeHero's Manga Shakespeare series. Other titles include *The Tempest*, *Richard III*, *Othello* and *Romeo and Juliet*.

Joanna Zhou, *Carlos & Sakura* – Her cutie bunny and grumpy ol' hedgehog characters are now merchandised, appearing on T-shirts and mobile phone snuggies for TokyoToys.

Neill Cameron, cover artist of Volume One and *Bulldog: Empire* – Neill's been very busy, illustrating Shakespeare's *Henry V* for Classical Comics, *School for Survival* – a comic strip written by Ye Editor for BBC Online – and even working on manga for the Catholic church! London's Institute of Contemporary Art (ICA) used a page from his story as the cover of their brochure for the ComICA exhibition, also spotlighting *Best New Manga*.

Andi Watson, *Princess At Midnight* – Andi has a new comic book coming out – *Glister*, a 64-page, bi-monthly digest series starting in August 2007 from Image Comics in the USA.

Daniel Merlin Goodbrey, *The House That Wasn't Her* – *The Last Sane Cowboy & Other Stories*, a collection of Daniel's excellent oddball narratives, is available from AiT/PlanetLar. He's seeking an artist collaborator for more manga – so if you need a writer, get in touch. Hey Daniel, you should talk to Rainbow Buddy and Cubbie.

And things are already happening for many of the contributors to *Best New Manga Volume Two*. More on that next time.

WRITE HERE, RIGHT NOW

Some people think it's cheeky to entitle our book the BEST. Having read the stories included here, tell us if you think it isn't so. But also, if you yourself know of something (or someone) new and deserving that we haven't yet discovered, please do let us in on it or even better, show us. Be sure to get in touch and nominate your favourite stories or featured characters from this volume. Let us know whose work you liked the best, and why. This is your chance to influence the content of future volumes.

So write in to the editorial address below:

Best New Manga
Constable & Robinson
3 The Lanchesters
162 Fulham Palace Road
LONDON
W6 9ER, UK

Or send your emails to: editor@bestnewmanga.com. We can't promise to reply individually, but we will take on board all of your comments.

Thank you.